JEAN SIBELIUS

DUO

for violin and viola

ca 1891–92

FENNICA GEHRMAN

Music drawn by Juha Töyrylä
Cover design by Marja Arvola and Pirkko Huttunen
Cover photo: Sibelius Museum, Turku, Finland

ISMN 979-0-55009-250-1

Printed by Painojussit Oy, Kerava 2020

JEAN SIBELIUS
Duo for violin and viola C major

It has long been known that Sibelius wrote a substantial number of chamber music works before turning his attention to orchestral writing. In a communication with Otto Andersson in 1915, he tells of how during his youth he had written several piano trios, the string quartets in A minor and B flat major and a quintet in G minor. But while it was known that Sibelius had written these works, the nature of the works themselves remained a mystery, for from the beginning of the 1890's onwards Sibelius guarded the scores closely and never made them available for public scrutiny. Furthermore, over the years, some of the scores have been lost. Sibelius made an exception out of the B flat major quartet, to which he gave the opus number 4. This was performed from time to time from a manuscript copy.

Finally, in 1982, the Sibelius family donated all the manuscript material in their possession to Helsinki University, where it was deposited in the library collections. Only after careful organisation of the completely unsorted collection did it become clear what a veritable treasure chest this collection was. For one thing it contained nearly the whole of Sibelius's youthful oeuvre. In addition to many of the works of whose existence was known, there were also many previously unheard of pieces.

The University collection shows that Sibelius composed a substantial body of chamber music, representing a particular period in his career (1883-91), before he composed his first major orchestral work Kullervo (1892). More than ten large-scale works and several tens of smaller pieces survive from this period. They vary greatly in quality and style and show Sibelius' development as a composer.

Practical considerations played a part in bringing these works into being. Besides musically ambitious works such as the A minor string quartet, there are virtuoso violin pieces for Sibelius's own use, trios written for the Sibelius family offspring (Jean, Christian and Linda), and pieces written for various occasions. Many of the smaller works were probably compositional exercises. The line which divides exercises from works of music proper is a difficult one to draw, especially since Sibelius himself gives no indication of what the criteria might be; it seems that he himself did not care much for many of the pieces we now regard as important, while it is known that many of the less weighty exercises did get performances.

In the works from the latter years of this period (1888-91) one finds features in common which were to come into their own in Sibelius's later output. Sibelius also made use of thematic material from these early works while composing during his mature years. The early Sibelius works now appearing in Edition Fazer catalogue are taken from precisely this later youthful period and all the original manuscripts can be found in the Helsinki University collection.

No score of the Duo for Violin and Viola has survived — only the parts written in Sibelius's own hand. On the back of the viola part the composer has written, with his ageing hand, the date "1886?". Research has shown however that the year of composition was somewhat later, either 1891 or '92.

The violin part is easy and simple in character and the viola performs a strictly accompanimental role. It seems likely therefore that Sibelius wrote it as an exercise for an instrumental pupil; the pupil may have played the violin line and he the viola, since he was proficient also in this latter instrument. The teacher-pupil theory fits in well with the year of composition, since at that time Sibelius found it necessary to augment his income by giving violin lessons.

Kari Kilpeläinen
English translation Andrew Bentley

Editorial note

Dotted slurs as well as markings in square brackets [ ] are editorial.

Bars 31-32 in the original viola part:

Duo in C major

JEAN SIBELIUS (1891-92)

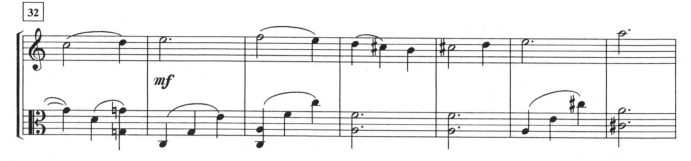

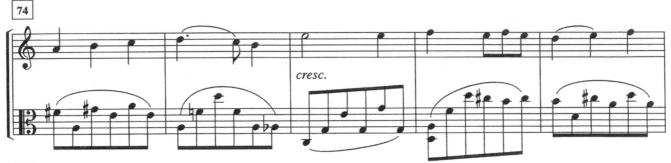

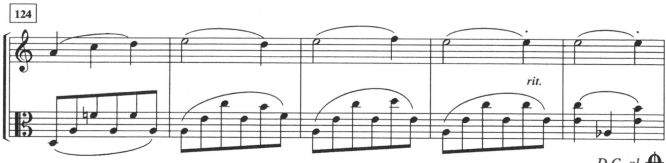

D.C. al ⊕

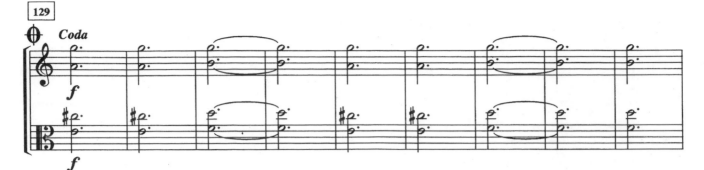

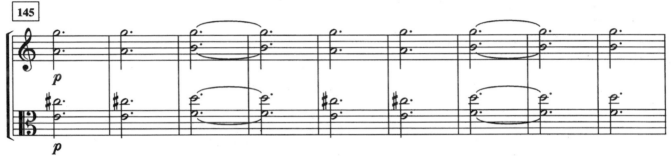

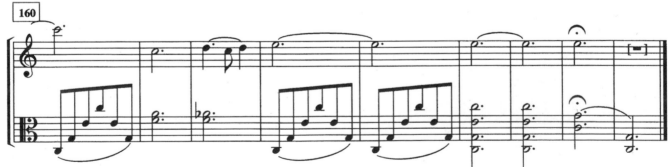